GREAT STORIES IN EASY ENGLISH

ROBINSON CRUSOE

Daniel Defoe

Abridged and Simplified by

S.E. PACES

S. CHAND
AN ISO 9001: 2000 COMPANY

D0226965

S. CHAND & COMPANY LTD.

7361, Ram Nagar, New Delhi-110 055

S. CHAND & COMPANY LTD.

(An ISO 9001 : 2000 Company)
Head Office : 7361, RAM NAGAR, NEW DELHI - 110 055
Phones : 23672080-81-82; Fax : 91-11-23677446
Shop at: **schandgroup.com**
E-mail: **schand@vsnl.com**

Branches :

- 1st Floor, Heritage, Near Gujarat Vidhyapeeth, Ashram Road, **Ahmedabad**-380 014. Ph. 27541965, 27542369..
- No. 6, Ahuja Chambers, 1st Cross, Kumara Krupa Road, **Bangalore**-560001. Ph : 22268048, 22354008
- 152, Anna Salai, **Chennai**-600002. Ph : 28460026
- S.C.O. 6, 7 & 8, Sector 9D, **Chandigarh**-160017, Ph-2749376, 2749377
- 1st Floor, Bhartia Tower, Badambadi, **Cuttack**-753 009, Ph-2332580; 2332581
- 1st Floor, 52-A, Rajpur Road, **Dehradun**-248 011. Ph : 2740889, 2740861
- Pan Bazar, **Guwahati**-781 001. Ph : 2522155
- Sultan Bazar, **Hyderabad**-500 195. Ph : 24651135, 24744815
- Mai Hiran Gate, **Jalandhar** - 144008 . Ph. 2401630
- 613-7, M.G. Road, Ernakulam, **Kochi**-682035. Ph : 2381740
- 285/J, Bipin Bihari Ganguli Street, **Kolkata**-700 012. Ph : 22367459, 22373914
- Mahabeer Market, 25 Gwynne Road, Aminabad, **Lucknow**-226 018. Ph : 2226801, 2284815
- Blackie House, 103/5, Walchand Hirachand Marg , Opp. G.P.O., **Mumbai**-400 001. Ph : 22690881, 22610885
- 3, Gandhi Sagar East, **Nagpur**-440 002. Ph : 2723901
- 104, Citicentre Ashok, Govind Mitra Road, **Patna**-800 004. Ph : 2671366, 2302100

Marketing Offices :
- 238-A M.P. Nagar, Zone 1, **Bhopal** - 462011. Ph : 5274723
- A-14 Janta Store Shopping Complex, University Marg, Bapu Nagar, **Jaipur** - 302015, Phone : 0141-2709153

ISBN : 81-219-2257-7

PRINTED IN INDIA

By Rajendra Ravindra Printers (Pvt.) Ltd., 7361, Ram Nagar, New Delhi-110 055 and published by S. Chand & Company Ltd., 7361, Ram Nagar, New Delhi-110 055.

CONTENTS

INTRODUCTION

D
ANIEL DEFOE was born in England more than 300 years ago, living from 1660 to 1731. Though he had some military adventures when he was young, he tried hard to be successful as a businessman. In 1700 he settled down in London and from that time worked as a writer. When he died, he was quite prosperous.

"*Robinson. Crusoe*" was written in 1719 when Defoe was nearly 60 years old. Around that time Alexander Selkirk, a sailor who had spent four years alone on the Pacific island of Juan Fernandez west of Chile, returned to England. This gave Defoe the idea for his story. Many readers accepted it as true because it is filled with such convincing details about Robinson's lonely life on the imaginary isle.

The theme of the story is self-reliance. Though he is thrown into a serious situation, Robinson overcomes every difficulty with his initiative and intelligence. He even manages to rescue others from danger. In the end he is rewarded by being rescued himself.

Defoe wrote many other books but today he is chiefly remembered as the author of

"Robinson Crusoe".

ROBINSON CRUSOE

I was born in the city of York in the year 1632. When I was still a boy, I wanted to go to sea. But my father would not let me go. I stayed at home till I was a young man. Then some friends asked me to go to sea with them. I went. Without asking my father, without asking God to help me, I went to sea.

Our ship was a small one, carrying fifteen men. It was sailing to Africa. At the beginning, the weather was good

and the winds favourable. Later on, a terrible storm arose. Our ship was driven here and there. Its sails were torn and some parts of the ship were broken. For twelve days the storm continued. On the thirteenth day, we sighted land.

"Land!" we all shouted with great joy.

At that very moment, our ship ran on to some rocks. The

sea began to pour in through a hole in its side. We left the ship and got into a small boat. How hard we rowed to reach the shore! We were nearly there when a wave, as high as a hill, crashed down on us. Our little boat turned over and all of us were thrown into the angry sea.

I sank but soon rose to the top of the water. With all my strength I swam towards the shore. The waves threw me on to some rocks. I held on to one of them till I felt stronger. Then I pulled myself out of the water and climbed over the

rocks to dry land. There I sank down and lay for a time without moving. I felt dead tired.

After a time I felt thirsty. I got up and walked about till I came to a small stream. The water was fresh and I drank plenty of it. I was hungry but I had nothing to eat. My pockets held only a small knife, a pipe and some tobacco.

Night was coming on. I had to find a place to sleep. I decided to sleep in a large tree. There I should be safe from wild animals. I made myself comfortable among its branches. To stop my hunger I chewed some tobacco. At that moment I fell asleep.

2

When I awoke the next morning, the storm was over. The sea was calm and the sun was shining in a cloudless sky. From my tree I was able to see the ship. It was lying, a wreck, about half a mile away.

I climbed down and ran to the shore. I then swam out to the ship. I needed food and clothes and I hoped to be able to find them there.

The lower part of the ship was full of water, but the store-room was dry. This was very lucky for me. I broke open a box of biscuits and ate till I could eat no more. After that, I looked around me and found many useful things : seven guns, gunpowder, an axe and other tools, some clothes, some books and some barrels of food. I found some money too. But what was the use of money on this wild island?

I tied some logs of wood together and made a rough platform or raft. I used this raft to carry me and my goods safely to the shore. I guided it into a small stream and there I landed.

The next day I began to look for a spot where I could build a hut. I had to find a shelter for myself and my things. I climbed the highest hill that I could see. When I reached the top, I looked around me. I was very sad to see that I was on a deserted island. The sea was on all sides of me. I could

see no land at all except for two small islands about nine miles away to the west. Worse still, I could see no huts on the island. There were no fields either. There was nothing to show that men were living there.

With a sinking heart, I realised that I was on a deserted island. Nobody else was living there. There were plenty of birds, however. I did not know if they were good to eat. I shot one and found that it was not. I think that my gun was the first that was ever fired on that island. At its sound, thousands of birds rose into the air, calling and crying wildly.

3

At last I was able to find a suitable place for my hut. This was a little plain on the side of a hill. The hill had a cave in it. I decided that this cave should be my store-room. In front of the store-room I would live in a tent. This tent I would make

out of the sails of the ship. This I did. Then I built a fence round my home. In this way, I was completely shut in and quite safe. I carried all my goods here. I stored them in the store-room on shelves which I made from boards.

This work took me many days. While I was working I was thinking how the days were passing. I had to find some way of marking their passing. I made a post and fixed it in the ground. Then, in big letters, I wrote these words on it :

I CAME ON SHORE HERE ON SEPTEMBER 30th, 1659.

Each day I made a mark with my knife on the post. Every Sunday I made a longer mark. On the first day of each month I made the longest mark. This was my calendar.

I was beginning to feel pleased with myself. I felt even more pleased as I went on making things. I made a chair to sit on and a table to eat at. I also made a lamp. This I needed very much. Without a lamp, I could not work in the evening. I had to go to bed as soon as it was dark. And so I made my first lamp.

This is how I made it. Whenever I found any fat in my meat, I kept it. Then I made a little cup of clay dried in the sun. I filled the cup with fat, and that was my lamp. It lighted my hut in the evenings although the light it gave was a weak one.

4

I had been on the island for ten months when I caught a fever. The weather was hot but I was shaking with cold. I was too weak to go out to look for food. There was nobody to help me and I had no medicines. I grew so thin and weak that I thought I was going to die. However, I did not die. Little by little, I became stronger. I thanked the good God for making me well again.

When I was quite better, I decided to look at the other parts of the island. I followed the little stream where I had landed my goods. This led me to some green plains where wild sugarcanes were growing. I also found some grapes here. I ate a lot of these. Then I filled a basket with some of them. I planned to dry them. I knew that dried grapes, usually called raisins, form a good food.

I slept that night in a tree.

Next day, I travelled farther and came to the loveliest valley that I had ever seen. Orange and lemon trees were growing in it. Bright flowers were blooming every-where. Birds with bright feathers were flying here and there. This beautiful sight gave me great pleasure. I felt like a king. Indeed I was the king of this pleasant land. Then I became sad, remembering that I was all alone. There was nobody with whom I could share my pleasure.

This journey took me three days. I then went back to my tent.

The month that followed was the worst that I spent on the island. There was heavy rain every day and all the day. I could not move out from my tent. I could not go out to look for food. I had to live on dried grapes and some food that I had brought from the ship.

During this time, I was glad to be busy. I tried to make some pots. These I found very hard to make. I failed in my attempts very often. Many of my pots broke and fell to pieces. In the end, after two months' work, I succeeded in making several small pots and cups and also two large ugly

things-I can hardly call them jars. This is how I made them :

I shaped the jars in clay. Then I built a fire round them and on the top of them. I kept the fire burning till the jars were red with the heat. After five or six hours, I let the fire burn out very slowly. I stayed up all night, watching the fire. In the morning, I was delighted to find that the jars were firm and strong. I began cooking in them at once though they were still hot.

When the great rains were over, I found a surprising thing near my tent. Some English wheat was growing there! I was very surprised and wondered how it had come there. Then I remembered. Among the things that I had brought from the ship were some old bags. One of these had held wheat. I had shaken it outside my tent, in order to clean it. Some grains of wheat had fallen to ground. These had grown during the heavy rains. Now I had a dozen ears of real English wheat. I saved the grain and planted it till I had a field of wheat. I was then able to make some bread for myself. How good that first piece of bread tasted! How proud I was of it!

5

All this time I was thinking how I could get away from the island. If I had a boat, I could get to the next island. From there I could get even farther, Perhaps I could get to the mainland. Perhaps I could find a ship sailing to England. Such were my thoughts. I had to have a boat. I had to make a boat.

I decided to make one as the Indians did. I cut down a great tree. This was very hard work and it took me twenty days. Then, with my axe, I cut out the centre of the tree.

This was even harder work. It took me three months. Altogether, it took me nearly six months to make the boat. In the end, I was pleased with my work. I had a very fine boat, big enough to carry me and all my goods.

Now I had to get the boat into the water. This proved impossible. I tried very hard but I could not move the boat at all. "Well then," I thought, "if I can't bring the boat to the water, I must bring the water to the boat. I began to dig a

stream from the sea to the boat. I stopped when I realised that I needed ten or twelve years to finish digging such a stream. I was very unhappy to give up the work but I had to.

By this time, I had been on the island four years. My clothes were worn out and I needed new ones. I made a cap for myself from the skins of some rabbits. From goat-skins I made a jacket and trousers. My shoes were made out of skins and so was my belt.

I think that I looked very strange as I went about the island. I carried an axe and a saw in my belt. I carried a basket on my back and my gun on my shoulders. My face was very brown from the sun. The hair that grew on my head I cut from time to time with scissors.

6

This happened one day at about noon. I was walking along the beach when I saw the mark of a man's foot in the sand. I was astonished, and frightened as well. I looked around me, but I saw nobody. I listened, but I heard nothing. I went up the beach and down the beach. There were no other footprints.

"Is it true?" I asked myself. "Have I really seen the mark of a man's foot?" I went back again to look. Yes, there it was! The mark of a man's foot. How had it come there?

I hurried home, looking behind me as I walked. For several days afterwards, I stayed at home for I was afraid to go out. Then I went out to examine the footprint again. It was much larger than my own. Who had made it? A savage? A man-eater?

I made my fence

stronger. I made seven holes in my fence to hold my seven guns. I fixed my guns in the holes so that I could fire them all in two minutes. I did all this because I had seen the mark of a man's foot!

I still did not feel safe. And so I looked for a safer hiding-place. I found a cave high up in the rocks. It was quite dry. There I brought five guns and a barrel of gunpowder. I also made some candles to light the place. Every day I climbed to the top of a high rock nearby. From here I looked over the sea. I was watching for canoes, bringing savages to the island. If savages came here. In bad weather they might come here for shelter. Or they might bring their prisoners here, cook them and eat them. Such were their cruel ways!

It was now autumn and the time for me to reap my harvest of wheat. I started out before sunrise. Before starting work, I climbed up the hill to my watching place.

There, on the shore, I saw nine savages sitting round a

fire. Nearby were the two canoes which had brought them to the island. They had not made the fire to warm themselves for the weather was hot. They had made it to cook some human beings! They were now eating them. I watched them full of fear. After their meal, they began dancing round the fire. I saw them waving their arms. I heard them singing and shouting. They had no clothes on at all. At last, they jumped into their canoes and sailed away. I was very glad to see them go.

I went down to the beach where they had been. Their fire was still burning. Near it, I found many bones-bones of people! Hands and feet of men! The sight made me feel sick and weak. I ran back to the safety of my tent.

That horrible sight troubled me for a long time. I made up my mind to shoot the savages if they came again. But no more came for many months.

Early one morning I was surprised to see five canoes on the shore, on my side of the island. I could see no savages. However, I was certain that there must be twenty or thirty of them, for they always came four or six in a canoe. I climbed the hill

to my watching - place. Looking down, I saw thirty savages dancing round a fire. While they were dancing, they were waving long sticks which they use for fighting.

As I was watching, the savages pulled two prisoners out of their canoes. One of these poor fellows was at once struck on the head. He fell to the ground. The other prisoner was left standing by himself till they were ready to eat him. He seized this chance to run away. He ran for dear life- straight towards me !

Three of the savages ran after him. Now only the stream was between us. The prisoner jumped in and swam across it. Two savages swam after him. The third one went back to his companions.

I decided to save the poor prisoner. Running towards the two savages, I knocked one of them down with my gun. I did not want to shoot, because that would make a noise that would bring the other wild men, but when the second savage made a rush at me, I had to shoot him. He fell dead. The sound of my gun made the run-away prisoner stop and stand still. He was frightened and stood there without moving.

I called to him and made signs to him to come nearer. He

came a little nearer and then he stopped. A few more steps and then he stopped again. At last he came close to me. Then he knelt down and kissed the ground where I was standing. He laid his head on the ground and placed my foot on it. By doing this, he showed that he was my slave and I was his master.

The poor savage was astonished because I had killed a man when I was far away from him. He pointed to the dead man and said something to me. Of course I did not understand what he was saying, but I was happy to hear his voice. His was the first voice that I had heard for years.

The savage whom I had knocked down was not dead. He was now trying to stand up. Seeing this, my savage made signs to me to give him my knife. He took it and, with a single blow, cut his head off. We buried the bodies in the sand.

I took my new friend to my tent. There I gave him water to drink and bread and raisins to eat. I made him lie down for he was very tired.

After a while, the savage woke up and came to me.

Again he lay down on the ground and placed my foot on his head. Once again, he wanted to show that he was my slave. I decided to give him the name of Friday, because on that day I had saved his life. I taught him to call me "master" and to say "yes" and "no". I gave him some clothes to wear : trousers which I had brought from the ship, a coat made of goat-skin, and a cap made of rabbit-skin. At first, Friday was uncomfortable in his clothes. I changed them to make them fit better. Soon he was wearing them every day.

Friday became my honest servant and also a true friend. He was never angry and always did his best to please me. He loved me as a child loves his father. I am sure that he was ready to die for me. As for my gun, he treated that as a kind of god. I often found him talking to it. When I asked him what he was saying to it, he answered, "I am asking it not to kill me."

Then began a happy time for me. I taught Friday to speak English. He learned well. At last I had someone to talk to. Friday's company was a real pleasure. I liked the pleasant fellow very much. He was a great help to me. I taught him to use a gun. I gave him a knife and an axe to carry in his belt. Time was passing happily now.

One morning, I sent Friday to the beach to look for sea animals called turtles and their eggs. He soon came running back, shouting :

"O master ! O master ! O bad, bad!"

"What is the matter ?" I asked him.

He pointed towards the shore.

"Look, master ! One, two, three boats. One, two, three."

Friday meant that three canoes had come to our shore. He was shaking with fear. He was always afraid that the savages would return. They would catch him, cut him to pieces and eat him.

"Don't be afraid, Friday," I said. "If they eat you, they'll eat me as well. But they're not going to eat us. Get the guns. You can shoot, can't you ?"

"Yes, master, Me shoot : But many come."

"Never mind, Friday. We'll frighten them with our guns and they'll run away. Will you stand by me and do as I do ?"

"Me die when you tell me, master," the good fellow told me.

I made three guns ready for Friday and three for myself. We climbed the hill to our watching - place. From there, we saw twenty-one savages, two prisoners and three canoes. I told Friday not to shoot till I gave the order.

"Follow me," I ordered him.

We walked down the hill and through a wood, hiding among the trees. Soon we were quite near the savages. They could not see us, because the trees hid us. But we could see them clearly. They were sitting round a fire, eating one of their prisoners. Another prisoner was tied up on the sand near them. They were going to eat him next.

Four of the savages got up and left the circle round the fire. They walked towards their prisoner. They began to untie him, ready to lead him to his death.

9

" Now, Friday," I said softly, "do as I do."

I put one of my guns on the ground. Friday did the same. I pointed a gun at the savages.

"Are you ready, Friday?"

"Yes."

"Fire !"

Friday fired and so did I.

Friday killed two of the savages and wounded three. I did not shoot as well as he. I killed one and wounded two.

The savages were very frightened. All of them, who were unhurt, jumped to their feet. They did not know where to look or where to run. They did not know what to do.

All this time, Friday was watching me closely. I threw down my empty gun. I picked up the other one. He did the same.

"Are you ready, Friday?"

"Yes."

"Fire !" I shouted. I fired and so did Friday. Two more savages were killed and many were wounded. They ran about shouting and screaming wildly.

"Now, Friday, follow me," I said.

I took my gun and appeared before the savages, with Friday close behind me. As soon as the savages saw me, I shouted. This further frightened them and they all ran off to their canoes. Friday ran after them, firing as he ran. He killed several more. The rest paddled away for dear life.

I ran towards the prisoner and untied his hands and feet. He cried out in fear for he thought that I had come to kill him. I told Friday to tell him that he was safe.

When Friday saw the savage's face, he took him in his arms and kissed him. He jumped up and down, singing and laughing. His actions were so strange that I thought he had gone mad. At last, when he was able to speak, he said to me:

"This man, my father."

It was Friday's father whom we had saved. Friday ran home to bring his father water and bread. When his father had drunk and eaten, Friday carried him to a canoe. He paddled the canoe to a spot near our home. His father was too weak to walk and so Friday carried him in his arms to the tent. Carefully he laid him down on a bed of straw.

While the old man was sleeping. I was preparing a good meal for him. Friday killed a young goat. I made a thick soup of this meat, adding a lot of rice to it. I cooked it on a fire outside the tent.

We all sat down at the table inside the tent. It was a happy meal. Friday was happy because he had found his father. His father was happy because he was safe with his son. I was happy because I had a new companion.

It was not long before Friday's father became homesick. He wanted to go back to his home which was on another island. And so I got a canoe ready for him and for Friday who was taking him home. I put water, bread and raisins in the canoe. I gave both Friday and his father a gun to take with them. With great sadness, I watched them go.

I felt very lonely while Friday was away. He came back in a week's time. I was asleep when he returned. He rushed into my tent shouting wildly,

"Master, master, they are here!"

Did he mean the savages? I jumped up, dressed in a hurry and went out to see who were there. Looking out to sea, I saw a boat coming towards the shore. I climbed up the hill in order to see better. Farther out to sea, I saw a ship. It seemed to be an English ship. The boat that I had first seen was the ship's boat.

I was very glad to see an English ship. But there was a doubt in my mind. What was an English ship doing here? If the sailors were English, they had not come here for a good purpose. I had better be careful.

Friday and I hid ourselves and watched carefully.

The boat reached the shore about half a mile away from us. It held eleven men. Of these, three were sitting with their hands tied together. They were prisoners. These three were roughly pushed out of the boat. They sat down  on the beach, looking very sad and worried. Six of the sailors began to walk about, exploring the island. Two men were left in the boat to guard it but they soon fell asleep.

I was very surprised to see all this. So was Friday. He said to me,

"O master! You see that English men eat their prisoners too."

"No, no," I told him. "They won't eat them but they may kill them."

Meanwhile, the tide was going out. Soon the boat was left high and dry on the beach. The sailors tried their hardest to push it back into the water. They could not, because the boat was too heavy for them to move.

"Leave it. It'll float when the tide comes in," shouted one of them.

In ten hours' time, the tide would come in. Before it come in, I was determined to have a talk with those three prisoners.

The sailors went into the woods to explore. Friday and I went home to get our guns. Both of us looked very fierce when we returned. We had a gun on each shoulder, two pistols, a knife and an axe in our belts. In our rabbit-skin caps and goat-skin coats we looked frightening. We made our way among the trees till we came near the three prisoners. Then, still among the trees, I called out to them,

"Who are you, gentlemen?"

The sound of my voice made all three jump to their feet in surprise. We came out of the wood. The sight of us frightened them. They seemed ready to run away. I spoke again:

"Gentlemen, do not be surprised at me. I am your friend. I have come to help you."

"Heaven has sent you then," said one of them gravely. "We badly need a friend."

I went on, "I am an Englishman and I wish to help you. I have one servant and several guns. Tell me how we can help you. Who are you? What has happened to you?"

"Sir," began the man, "I was the captain of that ship, but my men have been disobedient. They have fought against me. They were going to kill me and these two friends of mine. They then changed their minds and decided to leave us here to die on this deserted island. One of these men is my officer. The other is a passenger on the ship."

"Where are your enemies?"

"Over there, in the wood."

"Have they any guns?"

"Only two and one which they have left in the boat.

Three altogether."

"Good," I said. "Now come into the wood where we can't be seen. We must talk things over. We must make a plan."

When we were hidden from our enemies, I said to them. "I will help you if you promise me two things. First, you must obey my orders for I am the master here. Secondly, if we win back the ship, you must take Friday and me back to England."

"I promise," said the captain.

I gave a gun and a pistol to the captain and a gun to each of his friends.

It was now midday and the sun was very hot. I walked ahead of the others and found five of the captain's men asleep under some trees.

"Shall we shoot them all as they lie there?" I asked the captain.

"No," he answered. "Only two of them are bad. The others have been led away by them."

As we were speaking, two of the men woke and stood up.

"Are they the leaders?"

"No."

"Then let them go."

We fired and·killed the three others. The two we had not
fired were on their promise to help the captain, if he agreed
not to punish them. We tied their hands and feet together,
but we did not hurt them.

Three of the sailors who had not been with the others
heard the sound of our guns. They came running to see what
was the matter. When they saw what had happened, they
also promised to help the captain. We tied them up too.

Now we had five prisoners and three dead men. The
battle was over and we had won it.

12

I took the captain and his two friends to my tent. I showed them the things that I had made and I told them my story. They were very surprised.

"And now," I told them, "we must capture the ship."

"There are twenty-six men on board the ship," the captain

said. "We are few. How can we fight against so many?"

BOOM! The ship fired a great gun. A flag went up as an order to the sailors to return. Soon the ship would be sending another boat to find out what had happened.

We hurried to the boat which had brought the sailors to the shore. Quickly we made a hole in the bottom of it so that it could not be used. Then we saw a second boat, with

ten men in it, coming towards the shore. We watched it closely.

"Three of them are good fellows," the captain told me. "They've been led away by the others. Don't let us hurt them."

The sailors pulled the boat on to the beach. Then at once they ran to the other boat. They were surprised to find a hole in it. And they could find no sign of their companions. They shouted. They fired their guns. Our prisoners heard but they were too afraid to answer.

Seven of the sailors set out to search the island. Three men were left to guard the boat. A clever idea came to me then. I sent Friday with the officer into the woods. I ordered them to shout from time to time. Their shouts drew the attention of the men. They followed the sound. In this way,

they were led deeper and deeper into the island. Farther and farther they went from the boat.

When they were far off, we made a surprise attack on the three men in the boat. We easily made them prisoners. They were good fellows and promised to help us. We took the boat away and hid it.

The seven sailors returned from their search very late at night. They were tired out. To their surprise, they found that their boat had disappeared. And so had the three men in it. They shouted but there was no answer. Standing there in the darkness, they felt frightened.

"There is something very strange and frightening about this place," we heard them say. "Let's get away as soon as we can."

Then I ordered the captain and Friday to creep towards the leader who was standing with his two friends, a little apart from the rest. "When you get near, fire!" I told them.

They fired and killed all three instantly.

I ordered one of the men whom we had captured to speak to the sailors. He called out.

"Tom Smith! Tom Smith!"

Tom Smith answered, "Who is that? Is it you, Jones?"

"Jones it is," came the answer. "Throw down your guns or you are all dead men. The captain's here with fifty men. Your leader is killed. Will Frye is wounded and I'm a prisoner."

"Will they kill us?" asked Smith.

Then the captain called out, "Smith, you know my voice. If you lay down your guns at once, you will not be killed. This is my promise."

When they heard this, the sailors laid

down their guns and gave themselves up. They were taken prisoners and led away to the cave high up on the hill.

Next day, they begged the captain to pardon them. They also promised to help the captain to take back his ship. The captain set some of them free. However, five of them, whom the captain did not trust, were left prisoners in the cave.

Next day, the sailors mended the hole in the first boat. That night, the captain set out with twelve men to take back his ship. He found two men on guard on the deck. Then he ordered Jones to shout to them :

"We've found our men. They're all here."

The guards believed this. The captain and his men at

once climbed on board. They made the two men prisoners.
Their leader was on the deck. The captain shot him through
the head. Seeing that their leader was dead, the rest of the
crew agreed to obey the captain again. There was no more
fighting.

Seven guns were then fired from the ship. These told me
that the captain had taken back his ship. I was very pleased.
I had been watching and worrying for over two hours. At
last, I could lie down to sleep.

14

I was awakened the next morning by the captain's shout. He was standing on the top of the hill. I climbed up to him. He pointed to his ship, saying :

"My dear friend, there is your ship. She is all yours."

"At last I shall be free," I thought. I was too happy and too thankful to say a single word.

Friday and I went on board. I took with me some of the things that I had made. I left the island on the mineteenth of December 1686. I had lived there for twenty-eight years, two months and nineteen days.

I had no wish to sail any more. I only wanted to end my life in peace, in England.

QUESTIONS

CHAPTER 1

QUESTIONS

A. 1. Where was Robinson Crusoe born?
   2. When was he born?
   3. Who would not let him go to sea?
B. 1. What was the weather like?
   2. How long did the storm last?
   3. What happened to the small boat?
C. 1. Where was Crusoe thrown?
   2. What did Crusoe drink?
   3. What did he eat?
   4. Where did he sleep?

CHAPTER 2

QUESTIONS

A. 1. Where was the ship?
   2. Why was Crusoe going to the ship?
   3. What did he find in the store-room?
   4. How did he bring his things to the shore?
B. 1. What did Crusoe climb?
   2. What did he see from the top of the hill?
   3. Were there any men living on that island?

CHAPTER 2

QUESTIONS

A. 1. Where did Crusoe find a suitable place for his hut?
   2. What was his store-room?
   3. What was his tent made of?
   4. How did Crusoe make his home safe?
B. 1. What was Crusoe's calendar?
   2. What words were written on the post?
C. 1. What did Crusoe make to sit on?
   2. What did he make to eat at?
   3. How did he make a lamp?

CHAPTER 3

QUESTIONS

A. 1. What happened after Crusoe had been ten months on the island?
   2. What made him think that he was going to die?
B. 1. What was growing on the green plain?
   2. What did Crusoe see in that lovely valley?
C. 1. What made Crusoe stay in his tent?
   2. What had he to live on?

3. How did he make his jars?

D.   1. What "surprising thing" did Crusoe find?

     2. How had the wheat come there?

     3. What was Crusoe proud of ?

CHAPTER 5

QUESTIONS

A.   1. How long did it take Crusoe to cut down the tree?

     2. How long did it take him to cut out the centre of the tree?

     3. How long did it take him to make the boat?

B.   1. Was Crusoe able to get his boat into the water?

     2. Why did Crusoe stop digging the stream?

C.   1. What new clothes did Crusoe make?

     2. How did Crusoe look?

CHAPTER 6

QUESTIONS

A.   1. What did Crusoe see in the sand?

     2. Why did he stay at home?

B.   1. Where did Crusoe find a safer hiding-place?

     2. Where did he find a watching-place?

     3. What was not surprising?

     4. What were the savages' cruel ways?

C.   1. What did Crusoe see from his watching-place?

     2. What did he find near the fire?

     3. What made him feel "sick and weak"?

     4. What "horrible sight" troubled him?

CHAPTER 7

QUESTIONS

A.   1. How many canoes did Crusoe see?

     2. How many savages were there?

     3. What were they doing?

     4. What happened to the two prisoners?

B.   1. How did Crusoe save the prisoner?

     2. What frightened the prisoner?

     3. How did the savage show that he was Crusoe's slave?

C.   1. Why was the savage astonished?

     2. What did Crusoe do with the dead bodies?

     3. How did Crusoe treat his new friend?

D.   1. Why did Crusoe call the savage "Friday"?

     2. What did he teach Friday?

     3. What did he give to him?

CHAPTER 8

A. 1. What did Friday become?
2. What did Friday say to Crusoe's gun?
3. Why was Crusoe happier now?

B. 1. Why did Friday shout?
2. Why was Friday "shaking with fright"?

C. 1. What did Crusoe tell Friday?
2. What did he ask Friday to do?
3. What did Friday answer?

D. 1. What did Crusoe see from his watching-place?
2. What were the savages doing?
3. What were the four savages going to do?

CHAPTER 9

A. 1. What did Crusoe tell Friday to do?
2. Who was the better shooter?
3. Did the savages know what to do?

B. 1. Where did the savages run to?
2. What did Friday do when he recognized the prisoner?
3. What made Crusoe think that Friday had gone mad?

C. 1. Who was the prisoner?
2. Why did Friday carry his father?
3. What was Crusoe doing while the old man was sleeping?
4. Why was the meal a happy one?

CHAPTER 10

A. 1. What did Friday's father want to do?
2. How did Crusoe prepare for the going away of Friday's father?
3. How did Crusoe feel as he watched his friends leave?

B. 1. How long was Friday away?
2. What did Friday shout?
3. What kind of ship was coming towards the island?
4. What doubt was there in Crusoe's mind?

C. 1. How many men were there in the boat?
2. What did Friday say when he saw the English sailors?
3. What happened to the boat when the tide went out?
4. When would the tide come in?
5. What would Crusoe do before the tide came in?

CHAPTER 11

A. 1. What did Crusoe and Friday look like?
2. How did they approach the prisoners?
3. Why did Crusoe shout to them?

B. 1. What frightened the prisoners?

      2. What did Crusoe say to them ?

C. 1. Who were the prisoners?

      2. How had they come to the island?

      3. How many guns had the sailors?

D. 1. What promises did the captain make?

      2. What did Crusoe give to the three men?

      3. Where did they find five of the sailors?

E. 1. How many of the five sailors were shot?

      2. What did the rest of the sailors promise?

      3. What was the result of the battle?

CHAPTER 12

QUESTIONS

A. 1. Where did Crusoe take his friends?

      2. What did he show them?

      3. What must Crusoe and his friends do next?

      4. How many men were on board the ship?

      5. How did Crusoe and his friends damage the first boat?

      6. How many men were coming in the second   boat?

B. 1. Were the sailors able to find their companions?

      2. How many sailors went to search the island?

      3. How many sailors were left in the boat?

      4. What was Crusoe's cunning idea?

C. 1. Was the "surprise attack" successful?

      2. What made the sailors feel frightened?

      3. What did Crusoe order the captain and Friday to do?

      4. What happened when the captain and Friday fired?

CHAPTER 13

QUESTIONS

A. 1. What did Jones tell Tom Smith?

      2. What did captain promise the sailors?

      3. Did the sailors give themselves up?

B. 1. How many men went with the captain?

      2. Why did Jones shout?

      3. What did the captain do to the leader?

      4. What happened after the leader was dead?

      5. How did Crusoe know that the ship had been taken back?

CHAPTER 14

QUESTIONS

A. 1. What awakened Crusoe?

      2. What did the captain say to Crusoe?

      3. What did Crusoe think?

      4. When did Crusoe leave the island?

      5. How long had he lived there?

      6. What did he wish for now?